VOCAL SELECTION

ORIGINAL SOUNDTRACK SONGS FROM THE MOTION PICTURE

Folio © International Music Publications Limited
Southend Road, Woodford Green
Essex IG8 8HN, England

1–2–50202

04789424

Up a semitone, ie. In Eb

Grease

Words and Music by BARRY GIBB

13 bars in ¢ | y I solve my

G
Bm
They think our love is just a
We take the pres - sure and we
E
Bm
E
Bm
grow - in' pain. Why don't they un - der - stand it's just a
throw a - way. Con - ven - tion - al - i - ty be - longs to
F#m7
Em7
D
cry - in' shame?
yes - ter - day.
Their lips are ly - ing. On - ly
There is a chance that we can
C
Bm
E
Bm
real is real. We stop the fight right now. We got to
make it so far. We start be - liev - ing now that we can

F#m7
Bm
be what we feel.
be who we are.
Grease is the word.
It's got a groove.
Em7
Bm
It's got a mean - ing.
Grease is the time, is the place,
Em7
To Coda
is the mo - tion.
Grease is the way we are feel -
1. G
ing.

2. G
A
Em7
ing.
This is a life of il - lu -
F♯m7
G
sion, wrapped up in trou - bles, laced in con - fu -
F♯
Bm
D. S. 𝄋 (lyric 2) al Coda 𝄌
sion. What are we do - ing here?
Coda 𝄌
G
Bm
ing.

Hopelessly Devoted To You

Words and Music by JOHN FARRAR

A6
A
F♯7
I'm not the first to know there's
But, ba - by, can't you see there's
Hold on to the end." And
C♯m7-5/G
F♯7
1. Bm7
just no get - tin' o - ver you.
noth - in' else for me to
that's what I in - tend to
C♯m7
4 fr.
Cm7
3 fr.
Bm7
E7
I
2. Bm7
C♯m7
4 fr.
Cm7
3 fr.
Bm7
E7
do?
do.
I'm hope - less - ly de - vot - ed to

Dm
A
you.
But now there's
cresc.
Gm7
3 fr.
no - where to hide since you pushed my love a - side.
f
C7
3 fr.
F
Fmaj7
I'm out of my head,
A°7
D7-9
4 fr.
Gm7
3 fr.
hope - less - ly de - vot - ed to you,

C7-9
Dm
C♯+
hope - less - ly de - vot - ed to you,
Dm/C
Dm/B
Gm7
To Coda
3 fr.
C7-9
hope - less - ly de - vot - ed to
decresc.
Dm
A
D. S. (no repeats) al Coda
you.
My
mf
Coda
Gm7
3 fr.
C7-9
B♭m
F
hope - less - ly de - vot - ed to you.

You're The One That I Want

Words and Music by JOHN FARRAR

it's e - lec - tri - fy - in'!
Feel your way.
C
You bet - ter shape up, 'cause I need
I bet - ter shape up, 'cause you need
Em
a man
a man
Am
and my heart is set on
who can keep you sat - is -
F
you.
fied.
You bet - ter shape up;
I bet - ter shape up
C

Em
you bet - ter un - der - stand
if I'm gon - na prove
Am
to my heart I must be true.
that your faith is jus - ti - fied.
F
Noth - in'
Are you
left, noth - in' left for me to do.
sure? Yes, I'm sure down deep in - side.
You're the
C
one that I want.
You, oo,
Bb6

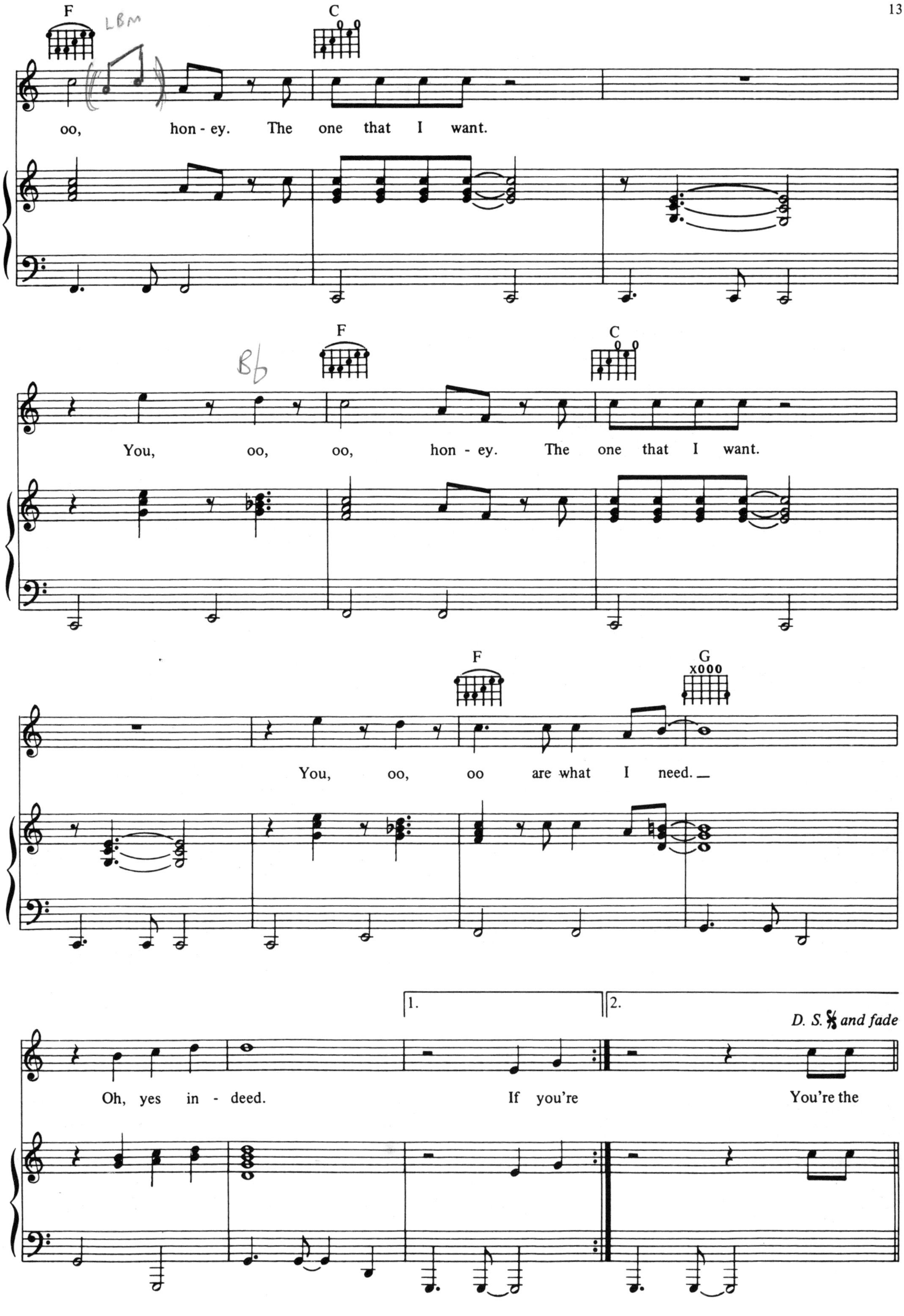

F C

oo, hon - ey. The one that I want.

F C

You, oo, oo, hon - ey. The one that I want.

F G

You, oo, oo are what I need. _

1. 2. *D. S.* 𝄋 *and fade*

Oh, yes in - deed. If you're You're the

Sandy

Words by SCOTT SIMON Music by LOUIS ST. LOUIS

F
Am7
Gm7
3 fr.
C7
San - dy, can't you see I'm in mis - er - y? We
Gm7
3 fr.
C7
B♭/F
B♭m/F
made a start. Now we're a - part. There's noth - in' left for me.
F
E♭/F
F7
E♭/F
F7
Love has flown. All a - lone, I
B♭maj7
B♭m6
F
Dm
Gm7
3 fr.
C7
sit and won - der why, oh why, you left me, oh

F
Eb/F
Bb
San - dy, oh San - dy.
Ba - by,
(spoken) Sandy, my darlin',
rit.
a tempo
Dm7
Cm7
3 fr.
F7
some - day, when high school is done,
you hurt me real bad. You know it's true.
Cm7
3 fr.
F7
Eb/Bb
6 fr.
Ebm/Bb
6 fr.
some - how, some way, our two worlds will be one.
But, baby, you gotta believe me when I say I'm helpless without
Bb
Ab/Bb
4 fr.
Bb7
Ab/Bb
4 fr.
Bb7
In heav - en for - ev - er and
you. (sung) Love has flown. All a - lone, I

E♭maj7
E♭m6
B♭/F
Gm
3 fr.
ev - er we will be.
Oh, please say you'll stay,
sit. I won - der why,
oh why, you left me,
Cm7
3 fr.
F7
To Coda
B♭
F7
D. S. (instrumental with spoken lyric) al Coda
oh, San - dy!
oh,
Coda
B♭
Dm7
E♭maj7
E♭m6
San - dy,
San - dy,
B♭
Dm7
E♭maj7
E♭m6
B♭maj7
San - dy,
why?
(spoken) Oh, Sandy!
rit.

Beauty School Dropout

Lyric and Music by WARREN CASEY and JIM JACOBS

Ab/Bb
Eb
Cm
3 fr.
Fm7
mf
Bb
Eb
Cm
3 fr.
Beau - ty school drop - out, no grad - u -
Fm7
Bb
Eb
Cm
3 fr.
a - tion day for you. Beau - ty school drop - out, missed your mid -
Ab
4 fr.
Bb
Eb
Cm
3 fr.
terms and flunked sham - poo. Well, at least you could have tak - en time to

Fm7
Bb
Gm
3 fr.
wash and clean your clothes up, af - ter spend - ing all that
Cm
3 fr.
Fm7
Bb
dough to have the doc - tor fix your nose up. Ba - by, get
Eb
Cm
3 fr.
Fm7
Bb
mov - ing. Why keep your fee - ble hopes a - live? What are you
Eb
Cm
3 fr;
Ab
4 fr.
Bb
prov - ing? You've got the dream, but not the drive. If you

Eb
Eb+
4 fr.
Ab
4 fr.
go for your di - plo - ma, you could join the sten - o
Db9
Eb
Cm
3 fr.
Fm7
Bb
Eb
pool. Turn in your teas - ing comb and go back to high school.
Cm
3 fr.
Bsus4
2 fr.
B6
Beau - ty school
E
C#m
4 fr.
F#m7
drop - out, hang - ing a - round the cor - ner store.

B
E
C♯m
4 fr.
A
Beau - ty school drop-out, it's a - bout time you knew the
B
E
C♯m
4 fr.
score. Well, they could - n't teach you an - y - thing. You
F♯m7
B
G♯m
4 fr.
think you're such a look - er. But no cus - tom - er would
C♯m
4 fr.
F♯m
B
go to you un - less she was a hook - er. Ba - by, don't

E
C♯m
4 fr.
F♯m7
sweat it. You're not cut out to hold a
B
E
C♯m
4 fr.
job. Bet - ter for - get it. Who wants their
A
B
E
hair done__ by a slob? Now your bangs are curled; your
E+
A
D9
4 fr.
lash - es twirled. But still the world is cruel. Wipe off that

E C#m F#m7 B E
an - gel face and go back to high school.
B E C#m
4 fr.
Ba - by, don't blow it. Don't put my
F#m7 B7-9 E
good ad - vice to shame. Ba - by, you know it.
C#m A B
4 fr.
E - ven Dear Ab - by'd say the same. Now, I've

E
E+
A
called the shot. Get off the pot. I real - ly got - ta
D9
4 fr.
E
C♯m
F♯m7
B
fly. Got - ta be go - ing to that malt shop in the
freely
sky. Beau - ty school
a tempo
drop - out, go back to high school.
E 6/9

Look At Me, I'm Sandra Dee

Lyric and Music by WARREN CASEY and JIM JACOBS

1. A
B7
E7
can't: I'm San - dra Dee.
2. A
E7
A
A7
heart to Dor - is Day.
(spoken) I don't
Dm7
G7
C
Am7
drink or swear.
I don't rat my hair.
Bm7
E7
A
A7
I get ill from one cigarette.
Take

Dm7
G7
A
F♯7
your filthy paws off my silky drawers!
B7
E7
Would you pull that crap with Annette?
D. S. 𝄋 al Coda 𝄌
Coda
A
E7
just plain San - dra
A
F7
B♭
B♭7/D
3 fr.
Dee.
(spoken) Elvis, Elvis,

E♭
C
C7/E
let me be! Keep that pelvis
F
F7
B♭
B♭7
far from me! Just keep your cool. Now you're
E♭
C7
B♭/F
start - ing to drool. (spoken) Hey, fongool, I'm Sandra
freely
Repeat and fade
F7
B♭
E♭6
Dee!
Repeat and fade
a tempo

Summer Nights

Lyric and Music by WARREN CASEY and JIM JACOBS

E A E A D G
GIRL: "Met a boy, cute as can be."_ Sum-mer days
"He showed off, splash-ing a - round."_ Sum-mer sun,
"We stayed out till ten o' - clock."_ Sum-mer fling
A B
1. 2.
Em7 A D No chord
drift - ing a - way_ to,_ uh, oh, those sum - mer nights._ Well - a, well - a, well - a
some - thing's be - gun._ But,_ uh, oh, those sum - mer nights._ Well - a, well - a, well - a
don't mean a thing._ But,_
D G E A D G
uh. Tell me more. Tell me more. Did you get ver - y far?___ Tell me more. Tell me
uh. Tell me more. Tell me more. Was it love at first sight?_ Tell me more. Tell me
E A D G A G
3.
Em7 A
more. Like, does he have a car?___ uh, oh, those sum-mer nights._
more. Did she put up a fight?_

Bb
Eb
Ab
4 fr.
F
Tell me more, tell me more. But you don't got to brag.
Tell me more, tell me more. 'Cause he sounds like a drag.
Shu - da bop bop. Shu - da bop bop. Shu-da bop bop. Shu - da bop bop. GIRL: "He got friend-ly,
hold - ing my hand." BOY: "She got friend - ly, down in the sand."

Eb
Ab
4 fr.
Bb
C
F
Bb
F
Bb
GIRL: "He was sweet; just turned eight-een."
BOY: She was good. You know what I mean."
Eb
Ab
4 fr.
Bb
C
Fm7
Bb
Sum-mer heat; boy and girl meet. But, uh, oh those sum - mer nights.
Cb
E
A
F#
B
Tell me more. Tell me more. How much dough did he spend?
E
A
F#
B
E
A
Tell me more. Tell me more. Could she get me a friend?

Slowly
D G A G D G
GIRL: "It turned cold - er; that's where it ends." BOY: "So I told her
mp
A G D G A B
we'd still be friends." GIRL: "Then we made our true love vow."
Freely
E A E A D G A B
BOY: "Won-der what she's do - in' now." Sum-mer dreams ripped at the seams. But,
Em7 A D G D
N.C.
oh, those sum - mer nights. Tell me more. Tell me more.
f

Greased Lightnin'

Lyric and Music by WARREN CASEY and JIM JACOBS

G
F
four - speed on the floor, they'll be wait - in' at the door. You
pis - tons, plugs, and shocks, I can get off my rocks. You
G
F
know that ain't no shit. We'll be get - tin' lots of tit in Greased
know that I ain't brag-gin'. She's a real puss - y wag - on, Greased
C
G
C
Light - nin'.
Light - nin'.
Go Greased Light - nin'. You're
burn - in' up the quar - ter mile.

F
Go Greased Light - nin'. You're coast - in' through the heat lap trial.
C
G
You are su - preme. The chicks - 'll
F
1. C
G
cream for Greased Light - nin'. We'll get some
2. Half as fast
C
F
C
Light - nin'.

It's Raining On Prom Night

Lyric and Music by WARREN CASEY and JIM JACOBS

Medium Cha-Cha
D
Bm
G
A7
It's
rain - ing on prom night; my hair is a mess. It's
wilt - ing the quilt - ing on my Maid - en - form, and mas -
run - ning all o - ver my taf - fe - ta dress. It's
ca - ra flows right down my nose be - cause of the
1. A7
2. A7
F♯m
storm. I don't e - ven have my cor - sage, oh

D7 G B7 Em7
gee. It fell down a sew - er with my sis - ter's I.
A7 D Bm G
D. (spoken) Yes, it's raining on prom night. Oh, my darling, what
A7 D Bm G
can I do? I miss you. It's raining rain from the skies, and it's raining real
A7 D B♭7 E♭
It's rain - ing on
tears from my eyes over you. Oh, dear God, make him feel

Cm
3 fr.
Ab
4 fr.
Bb
prom night. Oh, what can I do?
the same way I do now. Make him want to see me again. (sung) What can I do? It's
Eb
Cm
3 fr.
Ab
4 fr.
Bb7
rain - ing rain from the skies. It's rain - ing tears from my eyes o - ver
Eb
Cm
3 fr.
Ab
4 fr.
Bb7
you.
Ooh.
Rain - ing, ooh, tears from my eyes o - ver
Eb
Cm
3 fr.
Ab
4 fr.
Bb7
D. S. and fade
you. Rain - ing, ooh, rain - ing on prom night.

Blue Moon

Lyric by LORENZ HART Music by RICHARD RODGERS

D
To Coda
1. G
Em
C
love of my own.
real - ly could
love of my
D
2. G
C6
G
Blue care for.
And then
C6
sud-den - ly ap - peared be -
G
C6
fore me the on - ly one

G
C6
G
A
my arms could ev - er hold.
I heard some - bod - y
whis - per, "Please, a - dore
me."
But when I looked,

D7

— that moon had turned to gold. —

D. S. 𝄋 al Coda 𝄌

— Whoa, — blue —

Coda 𝄌

G Em C D

own, — with-out a love of — my

G C6 G

own. —

Mooning

Lyric and Music by WARREN CASEY and JIM JACOBS

Gm
3 fr.
E♭
F7
B♭
just moon - ing all o - ver you.
Gm
3 fr.
E♭
F7
(All o - ver who?)
Oh,
Cm7
3 fr.
F7
Dm7
I'm so full of love, as an - y fool can
Gm7
3 fr.
Em7-5
A7
Dm7
see, 'cause an - gels up a - bove have hung a

F7
Bb
Gm
3 fr.
Eb
moon on me. Why must I go on moon -
hind you moon -
ing, so all a - lone (so all a - lone)?
ing for-ev - er - more (for-ev - er - more).
There would be no more moon -
Some - day you'll find me moon -
ing if you would call me (up on the phone).
ing at your front door. (At my front door.)

F7
Cm7
3 fr.
F7
While ly - ing by my - self in bed, I
Oh, ev - 'ry day at school I watch ya.
Dm7
G7
1. Cm7
3 fr.
F7
cry and give my - self the red eye, moon - ing o - ver
Al - ways will un - til I got - cha
B♭
F7
2. Cm7
3 fr.
you. I'll stand be - moon -
rit.
F7
Cm7
3 fr.
B♭
Freely and much slower
B♭maj7
ing too. (There's a moon out to - night.)

Alone At The Drive-In Movie

By WARREN CASEY and JIM JACOBS

Gmaj9
Em7
Am7
D7
Bm7
E9
Am7
D7
G
Cm
3 fr.
G
G7
C
D
Gmaj7
G7
C
D
Gmaj7
G7
C
D

Bm7
Em7
C
D
Gmaj9
Em7
Am7
D7
Gmaj9
Em7
Am7
D7
Bm7
E9
Am7
D7
G
Cm
3 fr.
Gmaj9
freely
a tempo
rit.

Rock And Roll Is Here To Stay

Words and Music by DAVE WHITE

G7
C
It will nev - er die.
dig it to the end.
It was meant to be
It -'ll go down in his -
G
that way,
to - ry;
though I don't know why.
just you wait, my friend.
D
C
G
I don't care what the peo-ple say.
Rock-and - roll will al-ways be.
Rock - and - roll is here to stay.
It -'ll go down in his - to - ry.
D
C
G
(We don't care what the peo-ple say.
(Rock-and - roll will al-ways be.
Rock - and - roll is here to stay.)
It -'ll go down in his - to - ry.)

G G7

Ev - 'ry - bod - y rock. Ev - 'ry - bod - y rock.

C G D

Ev - 'ry - bod - y rock. Ev - 'ry - bod - y rock. Come

C G G

on. Ev - 'ry - bod - y rock. Now ev - 'ry - bod - y rock and roll.

G7 C

Ev - 'ry - bod - y rock and roll. Ev - 'ry - bod - y rock and roll, rock

G
D
and roll, rock and roll, rock and roll. Come
C
G
on. Ev - 'ry - bod - y rock and roll, roll, roll, roll.
G
Rock - and - roll will al - ways be. I dig it to the end.
If you don't like rock - and - roll, think what you are miss -
G7
C
It - 'll go down in his - to - ry;
in'. But if you like to bop and stroll,

G D

just you wait, my friend. Rock-and-roll will al-
come on down and lis-ten. Let's all start to have

C G G

ways be. It-'ll go down in his-to-ry.
a ball. Ev-'ry-bod-y rock and roll. Rock,

Em C

oh ba-by. Rock, oh ba-by. Rock,

D G

oh ba-by. Rock, oh ba-by. Rock!

Those Magic Changes

Lyric and Music by WARREN CASEY and JIM JACOBS

F
G6
G7
C
But if I_ don't hear it an - y - more,_ it's still fa - mil - iar to me;
but I'm sing - ing as I cry - ay - ay. While the bass_ is sound - ing,
Am
F
sends a thrill_ right through me. 'Cause those chords re - mind me of the
while the drums_ are pound - ing, beat - ings of my bro - ken heart will
G6
G7
C
Am
night that I first fell in love to those mag - ic chang - es._
rise to first place on the chart._ My heart ar - rang - es_
To Coda
F
G6
G7
C
Am
My_ heart ar - rang - es_ a mel - o - dy_ that's nev - er the same,_ a mel - o -
those_ mag - ic chang - es._

F G6 G7 C
dy that's call - ing your name and begs you, please, come
Am F G6 G7
back to me. Please re - turn to me. Don't go a -
C Am F
way a - gain. Oh, make them play a - gain the mu - sic I wan - na hear as once a -
G6 G7 C Am F
gain you whis - per in my ear. Oh, my

G6
G7
C
Am
F
darlin', ah hah.
Ee hee hee hee hoo
D. S. al Coda
Coda
hoo.
Oh, oh, oh,
oh, oh, yeah.
Oo
Fm6/A♭
3 fr.

Once through then repeat p. 62

Hound Dog

Words and Music by JERRY LEIBER and MIKE STOLLER

C
C
They said_ you was high - class._ Oh no, that_ was just a
F7
lie. Call_ you high - class. That_ was just a
C
G7
X000
F7
lie. Well,_ you ain't nev-er caught a rab-bit, and you ain't no friend of mine._
C
D. S. al Coda
Coda
C
No chord
C9
You ain't noth - in' but a

Born To Hand Jive

Lyric and Music by WARREN CASEY and JIM JACOBS

C
D
3 fr.
5 fr.
The doc - tor made Ma - ma lay down,
While chop - pin' wood, I'd move my legs,
F
D
A
G
8 fr.
with her stom - ach bounc - in' all a - round.
and I start - ed danc - in' while I gath - ered eggs.
E7
7 fr.
'Cause a be - bop stork was a -
The town - folk clapped. I was
D7
G#
4 fr.
To Coda
bout to ar - rive. Ma - ma gave birth to the hand jive.
on - ly five. "He'll out-dance 'em all. He's a born hand jive."

1. A
5 fr.
2. A
5 fr.
I could Born to
G/A
3 fr.
A
5 fr.
hand jive, ba - by.
Born to
G/A
3 fr.
A
5 fr.
D. S. (instrumental) al Coda
hand jive, ba - by.
Coda
A
5 fr.
G/A
3 fr.
A
5 fr.
Now, can you hand jive, ba - by?

G/A
3 fr.
A
5 fr.
Oh, can you hand jive, ba - by?
A7
5 fr.
Oh, yeah. Oh,
C7
3 fr.
D7
5 fr.
yeah. Oh, yeah.
E7
7 fr.
A
5 fr.
G
3 fr.
A
5 fr.
Yeah. Born to hand jive, oh yeah!

Tears On My Pillow

Words and Music by SYLVESTOR BRADFORD and AL LEWIS

Dm7
G
Dm7
G
1. C
Tears on my pil-low, pain in my heart, caused by you,
Am
Dm7
G
2. C
F
you.
you, you, you, you,
C
F
G7
C
F
G7
you.
Love is not a gadg-et. Love is not a
C
F♯maj7
Gmaj7
F♯maj7
Gmaj7
toy. When you find the one you love, he'll fill your heart with joy.

Ab7
4 fr.
A7
D
Bm
If we could start a - new,
Em7
A
D
Bm
Em7
I would - n't hes - i - tate.
I'd glad - ly take you back
and tempt the
A
Em7
A
Em7
A
hands of fate.
Tears on my pil - low,
pain in my heart,
caused by
D
Bm
Em7
A
D
you,
you,
you.
molto rit.

Freddy, My Love

Lyric and Music by WARREN CASEY and JIM JACOBS

A7
F♯m
F♯m7-5/C
2 fr.
day so much bet - ter, get - ting a sou - ve - nir or
tack when she catch - es those ped - al push - ers with the
pound - ing al - read - y, know - ing when you come home, we're
B7sus4
2 fr.
B7
Em7
Gm/C
3 fr.
may - be a let - ter. I real - ly flipped o - ver the
black leath - er patch - es. Oh, how I wish I had a
bound to go stead - y, and throw your serv - ice pay a -
D/A
G
D
Dmaj7
gray cash-mere sweat - er, Fred - dy, my love, Fred - dy, my love, Fred - dy, my
jack - et that match - es, Fred - dy, my love, Fred - dy, my love, Fred - dy, my
round like con - fet - ti, Fred - dy, my love, Fred - dy, my love, Fred - dy, my
G
To Coda
1. A7
2. D7
G
A7
love, Fred-dy, my love. love. Don't keep your let - ters from me; I
love, Fred-dy, my
love, Fred-dy, my

F♯m D7 Gm7 3 fr. A7 Dm
thrill to ev - 'ry line. Your spell - ing's kind - a crum - my, but, hon - ey, so is
Em7-5 A7+5 A7 Dm G7
mine. I treas - ure ev - 'ry gift - ie; the ring is real - ly nif - ty. You
Cmaj7 Bm7 Em7 A7
D. S. 𝄋 al Coda
say it cost you fif - ty, so you're thrift - y; I don't mind. Oh, oh, oh,
Coda
Repeat and fade
A7 D Dmaj7 G A7
love. Fred-dy, my love, Fred - dy, my love, Fred - dy, my love.
Repeat and fade

Rock 'N' Roll Party Queen

Lyric and Music by WARREN CASEY and JIM JACOBS

F
Bb
C
N.C.
They tell me her name's Bet - ty Jean, ah ha ha, rock 'n' roll par - ty queen.
Dm
Fri - day night and she's got a date,
go - in' plac - es, just - a stay - in' out late,
She's the girl that all the kids know;
talk a - bout her wher - ev - er she goes.
drop - pin' dimes in the rec - ord ma - chine, ah ha ha, rock 'n' roll par - ty queen.
I could write a fan mag - a - zine a - bout my rock 'n' roll par - ty queen.
Bomp ba bomp ba bomp ba. Oh, no. Can I have the car to - night?
Bomp ba bomp ba bomp ba. You should see her shake.

G7
C
Tacet
Ba - by, ba - by, can I be the one__ to love you with all of my
Ba - by, ba - by, don't you call it pup-py love. Don't you want a true ro -
C Bb Am Gm 3 fr. F
Bb C
might?__
mance?__
Ay yi yi yi. Rock-in' and a - roll - in' lit - tle par - ty queen._ We're
F Bb C F Bb C
gon - na do the stroll, hey, par - ty queen._ You know I love you so, my par - ty queen._ You're my
Bb C F
rock - in'______ and a - roll - in'______ par - ty queen.__________

There Are Worse Things I Could Do

Lyric and Music by WARREN CASEY and JIM JACOBS

Dmaj7
Bm7
E7
A7
good, I sup - pose it could be true. But there are worse things I could
D
D7
Slow Rock tempo, in 2
Em
Em/D
do. I could flirt with all the guys,
mf
Cmaj7
F♯m7-5
smile at them and bat my eyes,
B7
Em7
A7
press a - gainst them when we dance, make them think they stand a

Dmaj7
Bm7
E7
chance, then re - fuse to see it through. That's a
A7
D
Dm
thing I'd nev - er do. I could stay home ev - 'ry
Gm7
3 fr.
C7
night, wait a - round for Mis - ter
Fmaj7
B♭maj7
Gm
3 fr.
Right, take cold show - ers ev - 'ry day, and

A7
throw my life a - way on a dream that won't come
C/D
D7
Em
true. I could hurt some - one like me
Em/D
Cmaj7
F♯m7-5
out of spite or jeal - ous - y.
B7
Emaj7
I don't steal and I don't lie, but I can

C♯m7 (4 fr.) F♯m7-5 B7

feel and — I can cry: a fact I'll bet you — nev - er

Em7 Em7/D Cmaj7

knew. — But to cry in — front of

F♯m7-5 D7

you, — that's the worst thing — I could

rit.

Gmaj7 C Cm (3 fr.) Gmaj9 (5 fr.)

Tacet

do. —

a tempo *rit.*

Love Is A Many-Splendored Thing

From the 20th Century-Fox Motion Picture "Love Is A Many-Splendored Thing"

Lyric by PAUL FRANCIS WEBSTER Music by SAMMY FAIN

B7
E
C♯m7
4 fr.
G♯m
4 fr.
p
mf
E
E7
A
C♯7/G♯
4 fr.
F♯m
F♯m/E
E♯°7
C♯7
4 fr.
F♯m
F♯m/E
D♯m7-5
G♯7
4 fr.
C♯m
4 fr.
C♯m/B
5 fr.
A♯m7-5
5 fr.
E
C♯m
4 fr.
F♯m7
A
B7-9
E
rit.

We Go Together

Lyric and Music by WARREN CASEY and JIM JACOBS

Bb
Gm
3 fr.
Eb
F
Chang chang chang - it - ty chang_ shoo-bop, that's the way it_ should
be,
wha oooh, yeah!
We're one_ of a kind,_ like dip da - dip_ da-dip doo-wop da doo - bee doo.
Our names are signed_ boog - e - dy boog - e - dy boog - e - dy boog - e - dy

F
B♭
Gm
3 fr.
E♭
shoo-by doo-wop_ she-bop. Chang chang chang-it-ty chang_ shoo-bop, we'll al-ways
F
B♭
E♭
B♭
B♭7
be_ like one,_ wa-wa-wa-waaah._
E♭
When we go out at night,_ and stars are shin-in' bright_
B♭
E♭
up in the skies a-bove,_ or at the

C7
high school dance, where you can find ro-mance, may - be it
F
Repeat ad lib
B♭
Gm
3 fr.
might be love.
Vocal ad lib
Repeat ad lib
B♭
Gm
3 fr.
B♭
Gm
3 fr.
We're for each oth - er, like a
E♭
F
B♭
Gm
3 fr.
wop ba-ba lu-mop and wop bam boom, just like my broth - er is

Eb
F
Bb
sha - na - na - na - na - na - na - na yip - pi - ty dip de doom. Chang chang
Gm
3 fr.
Eb
F
chang - it - ty chang shoo - bop, we'll al - ways be to -
Bb
Gm
3 fr.
Eb
F
geth - er, wha oooh, yeah! We'll
Repeat and fade
Bb
Gm
3 fr.
Eb
F
al - ways be to - geth - er. We'll
Repeat and fade

Look At Me, I'm Sandra Dee (Reprise)

Lyric and Music by WARREN CASEY and JIM JACOBS

Dmaj7
B7
A/E
E7
A
scared and un - sure, a poor man's San - dra Dee.
A7
Dm7
G7
Cmaj7
Am7
Bm7
E7
A(addB)
A
Dm7
G7
Amaj9
F#7
B7

Printed in Great Britain by Hobbs the Printers Ltd, Totton, Hampshire 11/96